Schizoid Personality Disorder

Ashu Kumawat

2023 Ashu Kumawat. All rights reserved.

Table of contents:

Understanding Schizoid Personality Disorder

Schizoid Personality Disorder (SPD) is a type of personality disorder characterized by a persistent pattern of detachment from social relationships and a restricted range of emotional expression in interpersonal settings. People with SPD often experience social isolation, have difficulty forming close relationships, and may not experience pleasure from activities that are typically enjoyed by others.

Understanding SPD is crucial for anyone who may be dealing with this condition, or who has a loved one who is struggling with it. While the exact causes of SPD are not fully understood, research suggests that both genetic and environmental factors may play a role. SPD is also more common in men than women and often begins in early adulthood.

One of the hallmarks of SPD is a lack of interest in social relationships. People with this disorder may avoid social situations, have few close friends, and may not experience pleasure from social interactions. This lack of interest in social relationships can make it difficult for people with SPD to form romantic relationships or maintain close friendships. They may also struggle to understand social cues and may not feel comfortable in situations where they are expected to engage with others.

Another characteristic of SPD is a limited range of emotional expression. People with SPD may appear indifferent or emotionally cold, even in situations that would typically elicit strong emotional responses. They may also have difficulty expressing their own emotions, even in situations where it would be appropriate to do so. This limited range of emotional expression can make it difficult for people with SPD to connect with others and may contribute to their feelings of social isolation.

People with SPD may also have difficulty understanding and empathizing with the emotions of others. They may struggle to understand social cues and may not pick up on subtle emotional expressions. This can lead to misunderstandings and social awkwardness, which can further isolate people with SPD from others.

While SPD can be a challenging condition to live with, some strategies can help people with this disorder lead fulfilling lives. One important step is to seek out professional help, such as therapy or counseling. Therapy can provide a safe and supportive environment for people with SPD to explore their emotions and learn new skills for managing social interactions.

Another strategy is to develop coping skills to manage the symptoms of SPD. This may include mindfulness techniques, such as meditation or deep breathing exercises, which can help people with SPD become more aware of their emotions and increase their ability to regulate them. Exercise and other forms of physical activity can also be helpful, as they can improve mood and provide a sense of accomplishment.

It is also important for people with SPD to build a support network of family and friends who understand their condition and can provide emotional support. While it can be difficult to form close relationships with others, having a support network can help people with SPD feel less isolated and provide a sense of connection.

Finally, it is important to approach SPD with compassion and understanding. People with this disorder may appear cold or indifferent, but they are often struggling with intense emotions and feelings of social isolation. By approaching SPD with empathy and understanding, we can help reduce the stigma associated with this condition and provide support to those who are living with it.

In conclusion, understanding SPD is an important step in managing this challenging condition. By seeking professional help, developing coping skills, building a support network, and approaching SPD with compassion and understanding, people with this disorder can lead fulfilling lives and form meaningful relationships with others. While it may not always be easy, with the right strategies and support, people with SPD can thrive and find happiness in their lives.

Symptoms of Schizoid Personality Disorder

Schizoid Personality Disorder (SPD) is a condition that affects a person's ability to form and maintain social relationships. People with SPD often appear distant, indifferent, or emotionally detached in social situations. They may have difficulty understanding and expressing emotions and often have few close relationships. In this chapter, we will explore the symptoms of SPD in more detail.

The symptoms of SPD can vary from person to person, but some of the most common symptoms include a lack of interest in social relationships, limited emotional expression, and difficulty experiencing pleasure from activities that are typically enjoyable. People with SPD may also have difficulty understanding social cues, which can lead to social awkwardness and misunderstandings.

One of the most prominent symptoms of SPD is a lack of interest in social relationships. People with this disorder may avoid social situations and have few close friends. They may not feel comfortable in situations where they are expected to engage with others and may prefer to spend their time alone. This lack of interest in social relationships can be distressing for people with SPD, as they may feel a sense of social isolation and loneliness.

Another common symptom of SPD is a limited range of emotional expression. People with this disorder may appear emotionally cold or indifferent, even in situations that would typically elicit strong emotions. They may also have difficulty expressing their own emotions, even in situations where it would be appropriate to do so. This limited range of emotional expression can make it difficult for people with SPD to form close relationships and can contribute to their feelings of social isolation.

People with SPD may also have difficulty experiencing pleasure from activities that are typically enjoyable. They may not feel a sense of enjoyment or excitement from activities such as spending time with friends, going to parties, or participating in hobbies. This difficulty in experiencing pleasure can make it challenging for people with SPD to engage in activities that could potentially improve their mood or provide a sense of accomplishment.

In addition to these primary symptoms, people with SPD may also experience other symptoms such as a lack of motivation, difficulty with intimacy, and a tendency to be indifferent to praise or criticism. They may also have a limited ability to empathize with the emotions of others, which can lead to social misunderstandings and difficulty forming close relationships.

While the symptoms of SPD can be challenging, some strategies can help people with this disorder manage their symptoms and improve their quality of life. One important step is to seek out professional help, such as therapy or counseling. Therapy can provide a safe and supportive environment for people with SPD to explore their emotions and learn new skills for managing social interactions.

Another strategy is to develop coping skills to manage the symptoms of SPD. This may include mindfulness techniques, such as meditation or deep breathing exercises, which can help people with SPD become more aware of their emotions and increase their ability to regulate them. Exercise and other forms of physical activity can also be helpful, as they can improve mood and provide a sense of accomplishment.

It is also important for people with SPD to build a support network of family and friends who understand their condition and can provide emotional support. While it can be difficult to form close relationships with others, having a support network can help people with SPD feel less isolated and provide a sense of connection.

Finally, people with SPD need to approach their symptoms with compassion and understanding. SPD is a complex and challenging condition, and people with this disorder may struggle with intense emotions and feelings of social isolation. By approaching SPD with empathy and understanding, we can help reduce the stigma associated with this condition and provide support to those who are living with it.

In conclusion, the symptoms of SPD can be distressing and challenging, but with the right strategies and support, people with this disorder can manage their symptoms and improve their quality of life.

Causes and Risk Factors of Schizoid Personality Disorder

The exact causes of Schizoid Personality Disorder (SPD) are not fully understood, but research suggests that a combination of genetic, environmental, and developmental factors may play a role in its development. In this chapter, we will explore the various causes and risk factors associated with SPD.

One potential cause of SPD is genetics. Studies have shown that people with a family history of schizophrenia or other related conditions may be more likely to develop SPD. This suggests that there may be a genetic component to the disorder. However, it is important to note that genetics alone is not sufficient to cause SPD, and other factors are likely involved as well.

Environmental factors may also play a role in the development of SPD. Childhood trauma, neglect, or abuse may contribute to the development of SPD in some individuals. A lack of emotional support and nurturing during childhood can also lead to a child developing SPD as a way of coping with the emotional pain and isolation they experienced.

Another possible factor is developmental issues. People with SPD may have experienced developmental challenges, such as a lack of socialization during childhood, or difficulty with emotional regulation. These challenges can lead to the development of SPD in some individuals.

In addition to these potential causes, there are also several risk factors associated with SPD. One of the most significant risk factors is gender. Men are more likely than women to be diagnosed with SPD, although the reasons for this are not fully understood.

Another risk factor is age. SPD is typically diagnosed in early adulthood, although it may be present in childhood or adolescence. Older adults may also be at risk for developing SPD, particularly if they have experienced significant social isolation or trauma throughout their lives.

Personality traits may also play a role in the development of SPD. People who have a history of being introverted, shy, or socially isolated may be more likely to develop SPD. They may have difficulty forming close relationships and may be more likely to withdraw from social situations.

Finally, cultural factors may also contribute to the development of SPD. Some cultures may place a higher value on social relationships and interaction, which can make it difficult for individuals with SPD to fit in. In these cases, social isolation may be more common, which can contribute to the development of SPD.

In conclusion, the causes and risk factors associated with SPD are complex and multifaceted. While genetics, environmental factors, and developmental issues may all play a role in its development, it is important to remember that SPD is a complex and challenging condition that requires professional treatment and support. If you or a loved one is experiencing symptoms of SPD, it is important to seek out professional help and support to manage the disorder and improve the quality of life. By understanding the causes and risk factors associated with SPD, we can better understand the challenges faced by those living with this condition, and provide the support and resources needed to help them manage their symptoms and thrive.

The Role of Childhood in Schizoid Personality Disorder

Childhood experiences play a significant role in the development of Schizoid Personality Disorder (SPD). Children who experience neglect, trauma, abuse, or a lack of emotional support may be at higher risk of developing SPD as a way of coping with their experiences. In this chapter, we will explore the specific role of childhood in the development of SPD.

One of the primary ways in which childhood experiences can impact the development of SPD is through attachment issues. Attachment refers to the emotional bond that a child forms with their primary caregiver, typically their mother or father. Children who experience inconsistent or neglectful parenting may have difficulty forming secure attachments, which can impact their emotional development and ability to form relationships later in life.

Children who grow up in families with parents who have SPD or other related disorders may also be at higher risk of developing the disorder themselves. This is because children learn how to interact with others and form relationships with their parents, and if their parents have difficulty forming relationships, children may learn the same patterns of behavior.

Additionally, childhood experiences of emotional neglect or abuse can lead to a child developing SPD as a way of coping with the emotional pain and isolation they experienced. Children who do not receive emotional support and nurturing during their formative years may learn to suppress their emotions and avoid close relationships as a means of protecting themselves from further emotional pain.

Another important factor to consider is the impact of childhood trauma on the development of SPD. Trauma, such as physical or sexual abuse, can have a profound impact on a child's emotional development and ability to form relationships. Traumatized children may become withdrawn, emotionally detached, or hyper-vigilant as a means of protecting themselves from further harm.

It is important to note that not all children who experience neglect, trauma, or other adverse childhood experiences will develop SPD. However, these experiences can increase the risk of developing the disorder, particularly if they are not addressed and treated healthily.

Treatment for SPD often involves exploring and processing childhood experiences with a therapist or mental health professional. By examining the impact of childhood experiences on the development of SPD, individuals can gain a better understanding of their behaviors and thought patterns, and work towards developing more positive ways of relating to others.

In conclusion, childhood experiences play a significant role in the development of Schizoid Personality Disorder. Attachment issues, exposure to parents with SPD, emotional neglect or abuse, and childhood trauma can all increase the risk of developing the disorder. Understanding the impact of childhood experiences on the development of SPD is crucial for individuals seeking treatment and support for the disorder. By addressing and processing these experiences healthily, individuals with SPD can work towards developing more positive ways of relating to others and improving their overall quality of life.

How Schizoid Personality Disorder Impacts Relationships

Schizoid Personality Disorder (SPD) is a disorder that can have a significant impact on an individual's ability to form and maintain relationships. People with SPD tend to be emotionally detached and may struggle with social interactions, which can lead to difficulties in forming and maintaining close relationships with others. In this chapter, we will explore how SPD can impact relationships.

One of the primary ways in which SPD can impact relationships is through emotional detachment. People with SPD tend to have difficulty expressing emotions and may seem cold or indifferent in social situations. This can be perceived by others as a lack of interest or a lack of caring, which can make it difficult for them to form close relationships.

Another way in which SPD can impact relationships is through a lack of social skills. People with SPD may struggle with social cues, such as body language and tone of voice, which can make it difficult for them to understand the nuances of social interactions. This can make it challenging for them to initiate or sustain conversations, which can make it difficult for them to form meaningful relationships.

Additionally, people with SPD tend to have a limited range of interests and may prefer solitary activities. This can make it challenging for them to find common ground with others, which can lead to difficulties in forming and maintaining relationships. They may struggle with making small talk, participating in group activities, or sharing their interests with others.

Furthermore, people with SPD tend to be introspective and may spend a lot of time in their thoughts. They may find it difficult to connect with others on a deeper level and may struggle with understanding the emotions and perspectives of others. This can make it challenging for them to form close, intimate relationships.

Finally, people with SPD may have a fear of intimacy or close relationships. They may feel uncomfortable with physical touch or emotional intimacy, which can make it challenging for them to form close relationships. This fear of intimacy can stem from childhood experiences of neglect or abuse and may be a coping mechanism to protect themselves from further emotional pain.

It is important to note that people with SPD are not necessarily incapable of forming relationships, but rather may struggle with social interactions and emotional expression. With appropriate treatment and support, people with SPD can learn to improve their social skills, express their emotions more effectively, and form close, meaningful relationships.

Treatment for SPD may involve therapy or counseling, which can help individuals to explore and process their emotions and develop social skills. Additionally, medication may be prescribed to treat any underlying mental health conditions, such as depression or anxiety, which may be contributing to the symptoms of SPD.

In conclusion, Schizoid Personality Disorder can have a significant impact on an individual's ability to form and maintain relationships. Emotional detachment, a lack of social skills, limited interests, introspection, and a fear of intimacy are all factors that can contribute to difficulties in forming close relationships. With appropriate treatment and support, individuals with SPD can learn to improve their social skills, express their emotions more effectively, and form close, meaningful relationships.

Coping Strategies for Schizoid Personality Disorder

Coping with Schizoid Personality Disorder (SPD) can be challenging, but some strategies can help manage symptoms and improve overall well-being. In this chapter, we will explore some coping strategies for SPD.

Seek Professional Help: The first step in coping with SPD is seeking professional help. A mental health professional can provide a diagnosis, offer support, and help develop a treatment plan tailored to the individual's specific needs. This may include therapy, medication, or a combination of both.

Practice Mindfulness: Mindfulness is the practice of being present at the moment and paying attention to one's thoughts and feelings without judgment. Mindfulness can help manage symptoms of SPD, such as emotional detachment and social anxiety. Mindfulness can be practiced through meditation, breathing exercises, or other techniques.

Develop Social Skills: People with SPD may struggle with social skills, which can make it challenging to form and maintain relationships. However, social skills can be learned and improved through practice. Joining a social skills group or participating in therapy can help develop social skills.

Engage in Activities: Engaging in activities that are enjoyable and meaningful can help manage symptoms of SPD. People with SPD may have limited interests, but it is important to explore new activities and hobbies. Joining a club or group that shares similar interests can help find new activities to engage in.

Set Realistic Goals: Setting realistic goals can help manage symptoms of SPD. People with SPD may struggle with motivation and may have difficulty setting and achieving goals. It is important to set small, achievable goals and celebrate successes along the way.

Develop a Support System: Developing a support system of friends, family, and mental health professionals can help manage symptoms of SPD. People with SPD may struggle with social interactions, but it is important to maintain relationships with people who are supportive and understanding.

Challenge Negative Thoughts: People with SPD may struggle with negative thoughts and beliefs about themselves and others. It is important to challenge these thoughts and replace them with positive, realistic thoughts. This can be done through therapy, journaling, or other techniques.

Take Care of Physical Health: Taking care of physical health can help manage symptoms of SPD. Exercise, a healthy diet, and adequate sleep can improve mood and overall well-being.

In conclusion, coping with Schizoid Personality Disorder can be challenging, but some strategies can help manage symptoms and improve overall well-being. Seeking professional help, practicing mindfulness, developing social skills, engaging in activities, setting realistic goals, developing a support system, challenging negative thoughts, and taking care of physical health are all strategies that can help cope with SPD. It is important to remember that everyone's journey with SPD is different and what works for one person may not work for another. With patience, persistence, and support, people with SPD can learn to manage their symptoms and lead fulfilling lives.

Self-Awareness and Acceptance in Schizoid Personality Disorder

Self-awareness and acceptance are essential components of managing and coping with Schizoid Personality Disorder (SPD). In this chapter, we will explore the importance of self-awareness and acceptance in SPD and provide strategies for developing both.

Self-awareness involves recognizing and understanding one's thoughts, feelings, and behaviors. Individuals with SPD need to develop self-awareness as they often struggle with understanding and expressing their emotions. This can lead to emotional detachment and social isolation. Developing self-awareness can help individuals with SPD better understand themselves and their symptoms, which can be the first step in managing and coping with the disorder.

Here are some strategies for developing self-awareness in SPD:

Practice Mindfulness: Mindfulness is the practice of being present at the moment and paying attention to one's thoughts and feelings without judgment. Mindfulness can help develop self-awareness by allowing individuals to observe their thoughts and feelings without becoming overwhelmed or detached from them.

Keep a Journal: Keeping a journal can help develop self-awareness by providing a space to reflect on one's thoughts and feelings. It can also be a helpful tool for tracking symptoms and progress over time.

Engage in Therapy: Engaging in therapy can help develop self-awareness by providing a safe and supportive space to explore one's thoughts, feelings, and behaviors. A mental health professional can offer guidance and support in developing self-awareness and coping with symptoms.

Acceptance is another important component of managing and coping with SPD. Acceptance involves acknowledging and accepting one's symptoms and limitations without judgment. Individuals with SPD often struggle with feelings of shame and inadequacy, which can make it difficult to accept and manage their symptoms.

Here are some strategies for developing acceptance in SPD:

Practice Self-Compassion: Self-compassion involves treating oneself with kindness and understanding. Individuals with SPD need to practice self-compassion and avoid self-judgment and criticism.

Challenge Negative Thoughts: People with SPD may struggle with negative thoughts and beliefs about themselves and others. It is important to challenge these thoughts and replace them with positive, realistic thoughts. This can be done through therapy, journaling, or other techniques.

Focus on Strengths: Individuals with SPD often focus on their weaknesses and limitations. It is important to focus on strengths and achievements as well. Celebrating small successes and accomplishments can help develop acceptance.

Seek Support: Seeking support from friends, family, and mental health professionals can help develop acceptance. It is important to surround oneself with supportive and understanding individuals who can offer encouragement and validation.

In conclusion, self-awareness and acceptance are essential components of managing and coping with Schizoid Personality Disorder. Developing self-awareness through mindfulness, journaling, and therapy can help individuals better understand themselves and their symptoms. Developing acceptance through self-compassion, challenging negative thoughts, focusing on strengths, and seeking support can help individuals with SPD acknowledge and manage their symptoms without judgment or shame. With patience, persistence, and support, individuals with SPD can learn to develop self-awareness and acceptance and lead fulfilling lives.

Communication Skills for People with Schizoid Personality Disorder

Effective communication is a crucial aspect of any healthy relationship, including those of individuals with Schizoid Personality Disorder (SPD). Communication difficulties are a common symptom of SPD, making it challenging for individuals with this disorder to build and maintain meaningful relationships. However, with the right strategies, individuals with SPD can improve their communication skills and build more fulfilling relationships.

In this chapter, we will explore some communication skills that can be helpful for individuals with SPD to develop:

Active Listening: Active listening involves paying attention to the person speaking and attempting to understand their perspective. Individuals with SPD may struggle with listening and engaging with others, but active listening can help build better connections and understanding with others. Some active listening skills include maintaining eye contact, asking clarifying questions, and reflecting on what the other person is saying.

Direct Communication: Individuals with SPD may struggle with expressing their emotions or thoughts directly. However, learning to communicate directly and honestly can help build stronger relationships. Being clear and concise in communication can help reduce misunderstandings and build trust. Additionally, using "I" statements, such as "I feel" or "I think" can help express thoughts and feelings without placing blame on others.

Non-Verbal Communication: Non-verbal communication can be just as important as verbal communication. Individuals with SPD may struggle with non-verbal communication, such as maintaining eye contact or using appropriate facial expressions. However, non-verbal cues can convey emotions and intentions, so practicing non-verbal communication can help individuals with SPD better express themselves.

Compromise: Compromise involves finding a middle ground between two parties. Individuals with SPD may struggle with compromise, preferring to avoid conflict or confrontation. However, learning to compromise can help build stronger relationships and avoid misunderstandings. Compromise involves active listening, expressing one's own needs, and finding a solution that meets the needs of both parties.

Social Skills Training: Social skills training involves learning and practicing social skills in a safe and supportive environment. This can be helpful for individuals with SPD to develop communication skills and build confidence in social situations. Social skills training may involve role-playing, practicing active listening, and practicing non-verbal communication.

It is important to note that developing communication skills takes time and practice. Individuals with SPD may struggle with communication, but with patience, persistence, and support, they can improve their communication skills and build more fulfilling relationships. Seeking support from mental health professionals or support groups can also help develop communication skills and cope with symptoms of SPD.

In conclusion, communication skills are an essential aspect of building and maintaining healthy relationships. Individuals with SPD may struggle with communication, but by practicing active listening, direct communication, non-verbal communication, compromise, and social skills training, they can develop stronger communication skills and build more fulfilling relationships. With patience, persistence, and support, individuals with SPD can learn to overcome communication difficulties and lead fulfilling lives.

Developing Emotional Intelligence with Schizoid Personality Disorder

Emotional intelligence is the ability to understand and manage one's own emotions and the emotions of others. It involves being aware of one's own emotions, being able to express them appropriately, and recognizing and responding to the emotions of others. Developing emotional intelligence can be particularly challenging for individuals with Schizoid Personality Disorder (SPD), as they may struggle with expressing emotions and connecting with others. However, by focusing on developing emotional intelligence, individuals with SPD can improve their relationships and overall well-being.

In this chapter, we will explore some strategies that can be helpful for individuals with SPD to develop emotional intelligence:

Mindfulness: Mindfulness involves being present and aware of one's thoughts and feelings without judgment. Practicing mindfulness can help individuals with SPD become more aware of their emotions and how they are feeling in the present moment. Mindfulness can be practiced through meditation, breathing exercises, or simply taking a few moments to be present at the moment.

Identifying Emotions: Identifying and labeling emotions can be difficult for individuals with SPD. However, by practicing identifying and labeling emotions, individuals with SPD can become more aware of their emotions and learn to express them appropriately. One way to practice identifying emotions is to keep a journal and write down how one is feeling throughout the day.

Expressing Emotions: Individuals with SPD may struggle with expressing emotions, which can lead to difficulties in relationships. However, by practicing expressing emotions in a safe and supportive environment, such as therapy or support groups, individuals with SPD can learn to communicate their emotions effectively. This can involve using "I" statements to express how one is feeling and being honest and direct in communication.

Empathy: Empathy involves understanding and responding to the emotions of others. Individuals with SPD may struggle with empathy, but by practicing active listening and attempting to understand others' perspectives, they can develop greater empathy. Additionally, practicing empathy can help individuals with SPD build stronger connections with others.

Conflict Resolution: Conflict resolution involves finding a solution to a disagreement or conflict that meets the needs of both parties. Individuals with SPD may struggle with conflict resolution, but by practicing active listening, compromise, and empathy, they can learn to resolve conflicts healthily and effectively.

Developing emotional intelligence takes time and practice, but by focusing on mindfulness, identifying emotions, expressing emotions, empathy, and conflict resolution, individuals with SPD can improve their emotional intelligence and build stronger relationships. Seeking support from mental health professionals or support groups can also help develop emotional intelligence and cope with symptoms of SPD.

In conclusion, developing emotional intelligence is a crucial aspect of improving relationships and overall well-being for individuals with SPD. By practicing mindfulness, identifying and expressing emotions, developing empathy, and learning conflict resolution skills, individuals with SPD can develop greater emotional intelligence and build stronger connections with others. With patience, persistence, and support, individuals with SPD can learn to develop their emotional intelligence and lead fulfilling lives.

The Importance of Boundaries in Schizoid Personality Disorder

Schizoid Personality Disorder (SPD) is a condition that can make it difficult for individuals to form close relationships with others. As a result, setting and maintaining boundaries can be particularly important for individuals with SPD. Boundaries are limits that individuals set for themselves to protect their physical, emotional, and mental well-being. In this chapter, we will explore the importance of boundaries for individuals with SPD and some strategies for setting and maintaining healthy boundaries.

Why are boundaries important for individuals with SPD?

Individuals with SPD may struggle with intimacy and may find it challenging to communicate their needs to others. Setting boundaries can help individuals with SPD protect their emotional and mental well-being, maintain their independence, and build healthier relationships.

Setting Boundaries:

Setting boundaries involves identifying one's needs and communicating them to others clearly and directly. Here are some tips for setting healthy boundaries:

Identify Your Needs: The first step in setting boundaries is identifying one's needs. Individuals with SPD may have difficulty identifying their needs, so taking time to reflect on one's emotions and desires can be helpful.

Communicate Your Boundaries: Once you have identified your needs, it is important to communicate them to others.

This can involve setting clear expectations for others and expressing your needs directly and assertively.

Be Consistent: Consistency is key when it comes to setting and maintaining boundaries. It is important to uphold your boundaries and communicate them consistently to others.

Maintaining Boundaries:

Maintaining boundaries involves enforcing them and responding appropriately when they are violated. Here are some tips for maintaining healthy boundaries:

Say No: Saying no is a critical aspect of maintaining boundaries. It is important to recognize when something does not align with your needs and to feel comfortable saying no.

Practice Self-Care: Taking care of oneself is important when it comes to maintaining boundaries. Practicing self-care can involve setting aside time for activities that bring you joy, seeking support from loved ones, or engaging in self-care practices such as meditation or exercise.

Seek Support: Seeking support from a therapist, support group, or loved ones can help maintain boundaries. It can be challenging to enforce boundaries, so having a support system can be valuable.

In conclusion, setting and maintaining boundaries is crucial for individuals with SPD. Boundaries can help individuals protect their emotional and mental well-being, maintain their independence, and build healthier relationships. Identifying one's needs, communicating boundaries clearly and consistently, saying no, practicing self-care, and seeking support are all valuable strategies for setting and maintaining healthy boundaries. With practice and persistence, individuals with SPD can learn to set and maintain boundaries that promote their well-being and lead to fulfilling relationships.

Mindfulness Techniques for People with Schizoid Personality Disorder

Schizoid Personality Disorder (SPD) can make it difficult for individuals to connect with others and regulate their emotions. Mindfulness techniques can be helpful for individuals with SPD as they promote present-moment awareness and non-judgmental acceptance of one's thoughts and emotions. In this chapter, we will explore some mindfulness techniques that can be useful for individuals with SPD.

Mindful Breathing

Mindful breathing is a simple yet powerful technique that can help individuals with SPD ground themselves in the present moment. The technique involves focusing on the breath and observing the sensations of the inhale and exhale. When the mind wanders, gently bring your attention back to the breath.

Body Scan

The body scan is a mindfulness technique that involves bringing attention to different parts of the body and observing any sensations that arise. This technique can help individuals with SPD become more aware of their bodily sensations and promote relaxation.

Mindful Observation

Mindful observation involves bringing attention to one's surroundings and observing without judgment. This technique can help individuals with SPD become more present and aware of their environment.

Mindful Walking

Mindful walking is a technique that involves bringing attention to the physical sensations of walking, such as the feeling of the feet on the ground and the movement of the legs. This technique can be helpful for individuals with SPD as it promotes present-moment awareness and can be done outdoors in nature.

Loving-Kindness Meditation

Loving-kindness meditation is a technique that involves sending love and compassion to oneself and others. This technique can be particularly helpful for individuals with SPD as it promotes emotional regulation and can help cultivate feelings of connection and warmth towards others.

Incorporating Mindfulness into Daily Life

In addition to practicing formal mindfulness techniques, individuals with SPD can incorporate mindfulness into their daily lives. Here are some tips for incorporating mindfulness into daily life:

Slow down: Take time to pause and observe your thoughts and emotions throughout the day.

Connect with your senses: Focus on the sensations of your surroundings, such as the feeling of the sun on your skin or the sound of birds chirping.

Practice non-judgment: Observe your thoughts and emotions without judgment or criticism.

Take breaks: Take breaks throughout the day to breathe deeply, stretch, or engage in brief mindfulness practice.

Practice gratitude: Take time to appreciate the good things in your life and cultivate a sense of gratitude.

In conclusion, mindfulness techniques can be helpful for individuals with Schizoid Personality Disorder. Mindfulness techniques can promote present-moment awareness, emotional regulation, and feelings of connection toward oneself and others. Mindful breathing, body scans, mindful observation, mindful walking, and loving-kindness meditation are all effective techniques that individuals with SPD can practice. Incorporating mindfulness into daily life can also be helpful. By practicing mindfulness, individuals with SPD can cultivate greater awareness of their thoughts and emotions, and learn to regulate their emotions more effectively.

Schizoid Personality Disorder (SPD) can make it difficult for individuals to connect with others and maintain relationships. This can result in feelings of loneliness and isolation. However, individuals with SPD can overcome these challenges and cultivate meaningful connections with others. In this chapter, we will explore some strategies for overcoming isolation with SPD.

Seek Professional Help

One of the first steps towards overcoming isolation with SPD is seeking professional help. A mental health professional can provide guidance and support in developing social skills, managing symptoms, and addressing any underlying mental health concerns. Therapy can also provide a safe and supportive space for individuals with SPD to explore their thoughts and feelings.

Join a Support Group

Support groups can be a valuable resource for individuals with SPD. Support groups provide an opportunity to connect with others who are facing similar challenges, and can provide a sense of community and understanding. Support groups can also provide an opportunity to practice social skills in a supportive and non-judgmental environment.

Volunteer or Join a Club

Volunteering or joining a club can be a great way to connect with others who share similar interests. This can provide a sense of purpose and fulfillment, while also providing an opportunity to develop social skills and build relationships.

Practice Self-Care

Taking care of oneself is an important aspect of overcoming isolation with SPD. This can involve engaging in activities that promote relaxation and well-being, such as meditation, yoga, or taking a walk in nature. Taking care of physical health by exercising and eating well can also promote overall well-being and reduce feelings of isolation.

Challenge Negative Thoughts

Individuals with SPD may have negative thoughts or beliefs about themselves and their ability to connect with others. These thoughts can perpetuate feelings of isolation and hinder efforts to build relationships. Challenging these negative thoughts with positive affirmations can help individuals with SPD develop a more positive outlook and build confidence in their ability to connect with others.

Start Small

Building relationships can be challenging for individuals with SPD, but it is important to start small and take gradual steps toward developing connections with others. This can involve engaging in small talk with coworkers or neighbors, attending social events, or reaching out to old friends.

Set Realistic Goals

Setting realistic goals for social interaction can help individuals with SPD overcome feelings of overwhelm and anxiety. This can involve setting goals for the frequency and duration of social interactions, as well as setting goals for specific social skills to practice, such as maintaining eye contact or active listening.

In conclusion, overcoming isolation with Schizoid Personality Disorder is possible with the right strategies and support. Seeking professional help, joining a support group, volunteering or joining a club, practicing self-care, challenging negative thoughts, starting small, and setting realistic goals are all effective strategies that can help individuals with SPD cultivate meaningful connections with others. By taking small steps towards building relationships and practicing social skills, individuals with SPD can reduce feelings of isolation and develop a greater sense of well-being and fulfillment in their lives.

Building Connections with Schizoid Personality Disorder

People with schizoid personality disorder often struggle with forming and maintaining connections with others. Due to their tendency to withdraw and avoid social interactions, they may feel isolated and disconnected from the world around them. However, individuals with schizoid personality disorder can build connections with others and develop meaningful relationships.

Here are some strategies that may be helpful for individuals with schizoid personality disorder who want to build connections with others:

Start small: It can be overwhelming to jump into social situations, especially for those who are not used to it. Start by setting small, achievable goals, such as joining a club or attending a social event for a short period. Gradually work up to more challenging situations.

Practice active listening: When engaging with others, try to actively listen to what they are saying. This means paying attention to their words and body language and trying to understand their perspective. Active listening can help to build trust and connection with others.

Share your interests: Individuals with a schizoid personality disorder often have rich internal lives and a range of interests. Share these interests with others and try to find common ground. This can be a great way to start a conversation and build a connection with someone.

Find common ground: Look for common interests or experiences that you share with others. This can be a great starting point for building a connection. For example, if you both enjoy a particular TV show or hobby, use that as a conversation starter.

Join groups or clubs: Joining a group or club related to one's interests can be a great way to meet like-minded people. This can provide a structured and supportive environment in which to develop social skills and build connections.

Volunteer: Volunteering for a cause that you believe in can be a great way to meet people who share your values and interests. It can also provide a sense of purpose and fulfillment.

Use social media wisely: Social media can be a double-edged sword for individuals with schizoid personality disorder. On one hand, it can provide a way to connect with others without the pressure of face-to-face interactions. On the other hand, it can be a source of distraction and may contribute to feelings of isolation. Use social media in moderation and seek out positive, supportive communities.

Seek therapy: Working with a therapist can be a helpful way to develop social skills and address any underlying issues related to schizoid personality disorder. A therapist can provide support, guidance, and feedback on how to build connections with others.

It is important to remember that building connections takes time and effort. It is okay to start small and take things at your own pace. Don't be discouraged by setbacks or rejections. Keep trying and remain open to new experiences and opportunities. With practice and persistence, it is possible to build meaningful connections with others and create a sense of belonging in the world.

Understanding Empathy and Empathy Deficits with Schizoid Personality Disorder

Empathy is the ability to understand and share another person's feelings and emotions. It is a key component of social interaction and plays an important role in building and maintaining relationships. People with Schizoid Personality Disorder (SPD) often struggle with empathy, which can impact their ability to connect with others on an emotional level.

Understanding Empathy and Empathy Deficits in SPD

Empathy deficits are a common symptom of SPD. People with SPD may struggle to recognize or respond to the emotional needs of others, leading to social isolation and difficulty forming meaningful relationships. This can be due to a combination of genetic, environmental, and developmental factors that impact social and emotional development.

Research has shown that individuals with SPD often have reduced activity in brain regions associated with empathy, including the amygdala and anterior cingulate cortex. This can lead to difficulties in accurately identifying and responding to emotional cues from others, which may contribute to the social and emotional impairments associated with SPD.

Types of Empathy

There are three types of empathy: cognitive empathy, emotional empathy, and compassionate empathy.

Cognitive empathy is the ability to understand and recognize another person's emotions without feeling them oneself. Emotional empathy involves feeling the emotions of others as if they were one's own. Compassionate empathy is a combination of cognitive and emotional empathy, which involves both understanding and feeling another person's emotions while also feeling a desire to help and support them.

People with SPD may struggle with emotional and compassionate empathy, but they may still have intact cognitive empathy. They may be able to recognize the emotions of others but struggle to connect with them on an emotional level.

Impact on Relationships

Empathy deficits can make it difficult for people with SPD to form and maintain meaningful relationships. They may struggle to understand and respond to the emotional needs of others, leading to social isolation and difficulty developing close bonds. Additionally, their emotional detachment may be perceived as aloof or uncaring, further complicating social interactions.

Improving Empathy in SPD

While empathy deficits can be a challenging aspect of SPD, some strategies can help individuals improve their empathy skills and build stronger connections with others. Here are some tips for developing empathy:

Practice active listening: Actively listen to others and try to understand their perspectives and emotions.

Engage in perspective-taking exercises: Try to put yourself in another person's shoes and imagine what they are feeling.

Practice expressing emotions: Work on identifying and expressing your own emotions, which can help you better understand and connect with the emotions of others.

Seek out social support: Building strong social connections can provide opportunities to practice empathy and develop stronger relationships.

Participate in therapy: Therapy can provide a safe space to explore and work on empathy deficits, and a trained therapist can offer guidance and support in developing empathy skills.

Overall, empathy deficits can be a challenging aspect of SPD, but with practice and support, individuals can work towards improving their empathy skills and building stronger social connections.

The Connection between Schizoid Personality Disorder and Depression

Schizoid Personality Disorder (SPD) is a condition that affects a person's ability to connect with others on an emotional level, leading to feelings of social isolation and emotional detachment. As a result, people with SPD may be more vulnerable to developing depression.

Depression is a mental health disorder that is characterized by persistent feelings of sadness, hopelessness, and worthlessness. People with depression may also experience a range of physical symptoms, such as fatigue, changes in appetite, and sleep disturbances. Depression can be a serious condition that can interfere with a person's daily life, including their ability to work, study, and enjoy activities they once found pleasurable.

The relationship between SPD and depression is complex, and researchers are still working to fully understand the connection between the two conditions. However, some studies have suggested that people with SPD may be at an increased risk of developing depression compared to the general population.

One possible reason for this is that people with SPD may feel socially isolated and disconnected from others, which can be a risk factor for developing depression. Social support is an important protective factor against depression, and lacking it can increase the risk of developing depressive symptoms.

In addition to social isolation, people with SPD may also struggle with low self-esteem and feelings of inadequacy. These negative beliefs can contribute to the development of depression, as well as other mental health conditions like anxiety.

Another factor that may contribute to the link between SPD and depression is a shared genetic vulnerability. Some studies have suggested that there may be a genetic component to both SPD and depression, meaning that some people may be more predisposed to developing these conditions due to their genes.

Despite the link between SPD and depression, it is important to note that not all people with SPD will develop depression, and not all people with depression have SPD. Additionally, depression is a treatable condition, and there are a variety of evidence-based treatments available to help people manage their symptoms.

Treatment for depression typically involves a combination of medication, therapy, and lifestyle changes. Antidepressant medications can be effective in reducing symptoms of depression, while therapy, such as cognitive-behavioral therapy (CBT), can help individuals learn coping strategies and develop healthier thinking patterns.

For people with SPD, therapy can be particularly beneficial, as it can help them develop the social and emotional skills necessary to connect with others and form meaningful relationships. Mindfulness-based therapies, like mindfulness-based cognitive therapy (MBCT), have also shown promise in treating depression and may be especially helpful for people with SPD, as they focus on developing emotional awareness and regulation.

In addition to formal treatment, there are also a variety of self-help strategies that can help individuals manage their symptoms of depression. These may include exercise, healthy eating, and practicing relaxation techniques like yoga or meditation. It can also be helpful to connect with others who have similar experiences, either through support groups or online forums.

In summary, while there is a link between SPD and depression, it is important to remember that depression is a treatable condition, and there are a variety of effective treatments available. If you are experiencing symptoms of depression, it is important to speak with a healthcare professional who can help you develop a treatment plan that is tailored to your specific needs. With the right treatment and support, it is possible to manage the symptoms of depression and live a fulfilling life.

Addressing Negative Thought Patterns with Schizoid Personality Disorder

Negative thought patterns are a common feature of many mental health conditions, including schizoid personality disorder. Individuals with this disorder may experience negative thoughts about themselves, others, and the world around them, which can contribute to feelings of isolation and social withdrawal. However, some strategies can be used to address negative thought patterns and improve mental well-being.

Identifying Negative Thought Patterns

The first step in addressing negative thought patterns is to identify them. Common negative thought patterns in individuals with schizoid personality disorder may include:

Self-criticism: This involves negative thoughts about oneself, including feelings of worthlessness, incompetence, and self-blame.

Negative expectations: This involves anticipating negative outcomes in various situations and expecting the worst in oneself, others, and the world.

All-or-nothing thinking: This involves seeing things as black or white, with no shades of gray in between. This can lead to rigid thinking patterns and difficulty finding solutions to problems.

Catastrophizing: This involves anticipating the worst possible outcome in a situation and overreacting to it.

Replacing Negative Thoughts with Positive Ones

Once negative thought patterns have been identified, the next step is to replace them with positive ones. This can be done through cognitive restructuring, which involves challenging negative thoughts and replacing them with more positive and realistic ones.

For example, if an individual with schizoid personality disorder is experiencing self-critical thoughts, they may challenge these thoughts by asking themselves if there is any evidence to support them. They may then replace these negative thoughts with positive affirmations, such as "I am competent and capable."

Similarly, if an individual is experiencing negative expectations, they may challenge these thoughts by asking themselves if there is any evidence to support them. They may then replace these negative thoughts with more realistic expectations, such as "I may not know how this situation will turn out, but I can handle whatever comes my way."

Practicing Mindfulness

Mindfulness is another strategy that can be used to address negative thought patterns in individuals with schizoid personality disorder. Mindfulness involves paying attention to the present moment without judgment, which can help individuals become more aware of their thoughts and emotions.

By practicing mindfulness, individuals with schizoid personality disorder can learn to observe their negative thoughts without getting caught up in them. This can help them develop a more positive and compassionate attitude towards themselves and others, which can improve their overall well-being.

Seeking Support

Finally, seeking support from friends, family, or a mental health professional can also help address negative thought patterns. Supportive individuals can provide a positive perspective and offer guidance in challenging negative thoughts and replacing them with positive ones.

A mental health professional can also provide therapy, which may involve cognitive-behavioral therapy (CBT). CBT is a type of therapy that focuses on identifying and challenging negative thought patterns and replacing them with more positive and realistic ones. This can be a helpful tool for individuals with schizoid personality disorder who are struggling with negative thoughts and feelings.

Conclusion

Negative thought patterns are a common feature of schizoid personality disorder, but they can be addressed through various strategies. By identifying negative thought patterns, replacing them with positive ones, practicing mindfulness, and seeking support, individuals with schizoid personality disorder can improve their mental well-being and lead more fulfilling lives. It may take time and effort to break negative thought patterns, but with practice, it is possible to develop a more positive and compassionate attitude toward oneself and others.

Reducing Social Stigma and Misconceptions of Schizoid Personality Disorder

Schizoid Personality Disorder (SPD) is a complex and often misunderstood mental health condition. Those who live with SPD often struggle to connect with others and may feel misunderstood by the world around them. Unfortunately, negative stereotypes and stigmas associated with the condition can make it even more challenging for individuals with SPD to navigate daily life. In this chapter, we will explore the social stigma and misconceptions surrounding SPD and discuss ways to reduce their impact.

Social Stigma and Misconceptions of Schizoid Personality Disorder

Social stigma refers to the negative attitudes and beliefs held by society towards individuals or groups that are different from the norm. People with SPD often face significant social stigma, as their behaviors and ways of relating to others are not typical. Some of the common misconceptions and stigmas surrounding SPD include:

People with SPD are cold and unfeeling.

People with SPD are arrogant and self-centered.

People with SPD are incapable of forming close relationships.

People with SPD are dangerous or violent.

These stigmas can lead to isolation, discrimination, and a lack of access to resources for individuals with SPD. They can also make it more challenging for individuals with SPD to seek help and support, as they may feel ashamed or embarrassed by their condition.

Reducing Stigma and Misconceptions

Reducing the stigma and misconceptions surrounding SPD is essential for creating a more inclusive and supportive society. Here are some strategies for reducing the stigma and misconceptions associated with SPD:

Education and Awareness

Education is one of the most effective ways to reduce stigma and misconceptions surrounding SPD. By increasing awareness and understanding of the condition, we can break down stereotypes and foster empathy and compassion towards those who live with SPD. Educational initiatives can include public speaking, community events, online resources, and support groups.

Empathy and Compassion

Empathy and compassion can go a long way in reducing stigma and misconceptions surrounding SPD. By putting ourselves in the shoes of someone with SPD, we can better understand the challenges they face and offer support and understanding. Practicing empathy and compassion can be as simple as listening without judgment, offering a kind word or gesture, or volunteering for mental health organizations.

Language and Terminology

The language we use to talk about mental health conditions can have a significant impact on stigma and misconceptions. Using derogatory or stigmatizing language can reinforce negative stereotypes and make it more challenging for individuals with SPD to seek help. Instead, we should use person-first language that emphasizes the individual's humanity and uniqueness, rather than their diagnosis.

Advocacy and Support

Advocacy and support are essential for reducing stigma and misconceptions surrounding SPD. By speaking out against discrimination and advocating for inclusive policies and practices, we can create a more accepting and supportive environment for individuals with SPD. Support can include access to mental health services, support groups, and social programs that promote inclusion and acceptance.

Conclusion

Reducing stigma and misconceptions surrounding SPD is crucial for creating a more inclusive and accepting society. By educating ourselves and others, practicing empathy and compassion, using person-first language, and advocating for inclusive policies and practices, we can break down stereotypes and promote understanding and acceptance for individuals with SPD. It is time to remove the stigma and barriers that prevent individuals with SPD from receiving the care and support they need to thrive.

Developing a Support System with Schizoid Personality Disorder

Schizoid Personality Disorder (SPD) is a condition that can make it challenging to form and maintain social relationships. While it's essential to work on improving social connections and reducing isolation, it's also important to have a support system in place. A support system can provide emotional support, offer practical help, and give you a sense of belonging. In this chapter, we'll discuss how to develop a support system for Schizoid Personality Disorder.

Understand What a Support System Is

A support system is a network of people that you can turn to when you need help or support. This network can include friends, family members, mental health professionals, and support groups. A support system is essential because it can provide you with a sense of belonging, increase your self-esteem, and reduce stress.

Identify People Who Can Be Part of Your Support System

The first step in developing a support system is to identify the people in your life who can be part of it. Start by making a list of the people you trust, feel comfortable with, and can rely on. This list can include family members, friends, co-workers, neighbors, mental health professionals, and support group members.

Build Relationships Gradually

Once you've identified people who can be part of your support system, you can start building relationships with them. However, if you have SPD, building relationships can be challenging. Start by taking small steps, such as engaging in small talk or sharing a personal experience. As you become more comfortable, you can start opening up more and sharing your thoughts and feelings.

Join a Support Group

Support groups can be a great way to meet people who understand what you're going through. Support groups can be online or in-person, and they can provide a safe and supportive environment to discuss your challenges and successes. You can find support groups through mental health organizations, community centers, or online forums.

Seek Professional Help

Mental health professionals, such as therapists or counselors, can provide professional support and guidance. They can help you develop coping skills, manage symptoms, and improve your relationships. They can also help you identify and work through any underlying issues that may be contributing to your SPD.

Utilize Technology

Technology has made it easier than ever to connect with others. You can use social media platforms to connect with friends and family members who live far away or use online forums to connect with people who share similar interests. Additionally, many mental health apps are available that can help you manage your symptoms and connect with mental health professionals.

Conclusion

Developing a support system can be an essential part of managing Schizoid Personality Disorder. A support system can provide emotional support, offer practical help, and give you a sense of belonging. Start by identifying people who can be part of your support system and building relationships with them gradually. Joining a support group, seeking professional help, and utilizing technology can also help develop a support system. Remember, building a support system takes time, but the effort is worth it.

Overcoming the Fear of Intimacy with Schizoid Personality Disorder

One of the defining features of Schizoid Personality Disorder (SPD) is a deep-seated fear of intimacy. People with SPD often struggle to form close relationships with others, preferring to keep to themselves and avoid emotional connections with others. This can make it difficult to develop and maintain healthy, fulfilling relationships with others, and can leave people with SPD feeling isolated and lonely.

However, it is possible to overcome this fear of intimacy and form meaningful connections with others, even with SPD. In this chapter, we will explore some strategies for overcoming this fear and building intimate relationships.

Understanding the Fear of Intimacy

To overcome the fear of intimacy, it is important to understand where this fear comes from. People with SPD often have a history of trauma or neglect in childhood that has led them to become emotionally guarded and avoidant. They may have learned that forming emotional connections with others is unsafe or undesirable, leading them to retreat into themselves and avoid close relationships.

In addition, people with SPD may struggle with a lack of social skills or anxiety in social situations, which can make it difficult to form and maintain relationships. They may also struggle with emotional regulation, finding it difficult to express their feelings or connect with the emotions of others.

Strategies for Overcoming the Fear of Intimacy

Start Small

When trying to overcome the fear of intimacy, it is important to start small and take things one step at a time. Rather than diving headfirst into a close relationship, try to gradually build connections with others. This might involve attending social events or joining groups related to your interests, where you can meet others with similar passions and build connections slowly.

Practice Self-Awareness

Developing self-awareness is an important part of overcoming the fear of intimacy. This involves being aware of your own emotions, needs, and boundaries, and learning to communicate these to others. Take time to reflect on your feelings and needs, and practice expressing these to others clearly and directly.

Develop Communication Skills

People with SPD often struggle with communication, which can make it difficult to form and maintain relationships. Developing communication skills can be a key part of overcoming the fear of intimacy. Practice active listening, which involves fully focusing on the person you are talking to and reflecting on what they have said. This can help to build trust and create a more meaningful connection.

Learn to Manage Anxiety

Anxiety can be a major barrier to building intimacy with others. Learning to manage anxiety can help to reduce feelings of fear and discomfort, making it easier to connect with others. Practice relaxation techniques, such as deep breathing or meditation, to help reduce anxiety and promote a sense of calm.

Challenge Negative Thoughts

Negative thoughts and beliefs about relationships can be a major obstacle to overcoming the fear of intimacy. It is important to challenge these negative thoughts and replace them with more positive, realistic beliefs. For example, rather than thinking "relationships are dangerous and hurtful," try thinking "relationships can be challenging, but they can also be rewarding and fulfilling."

Seek Professional Help

If you are struggling to overcome the fear of intimacy on your own, seeking professional help can be a valuable resource. A therapist or counselor can help you to explore the underlying causes of your fear of intimacy, develop coping strategies, and work through any emotional issues that may be getting in the way of building intimate relationships.

Cognitive Behavioral Therapy for Schizoid Personality Disorder

Cognitive Behavioral Therapy (CBT) is a therapeutic approach that is effective in treating a range of mental health conditions, including Schizoid Personality Disorder (SPD). CBT focuses on identifying and changing negative thought patterns and behaviors that may be contributing to distress.

CBT for SPD aims to help individuals challenge and modify the maladaptive thinking patterns and behaviors that are characteristic of the disorder. The therapy involves identifying and understanding negative patterns of thinking and behavior, and then learning how to replace them with more positive and adaptive ones.

One of the key components of CBT is the identification of negative automatic thoughts, which are often irrational and self-defeating. In SPD, individuals may have negative thoughts and beliefs about themselves, others, and the world around them that contribute to their isolation and withdrawal. Examples of such thoughts may include "I am better off alone," "People are too demanding," or "Others will reject me if I open up."

CBT helps individuals identify these thoughts and learn to challenge them with evidence-based reasoning. For example, if someone with SPD has the thought "I am better off alone," the therapist may challenge this belief by pointing out times when the person has enjoyed the company of others or by exploring the potential benefits of social interaction, such as gaining emotional support and feeling connected.

CBT also helps individuals learn new coping skills and behaviors to replace negative ones. For individuals with SPD, this may involve learning social skills and practicing interactions with others, such as initiating conversations, sharing personal information, and expressing emotions. The therapist may also use role-playing exercises to help individuals practice these skills in a safe and supportive environment.

Another important component of CBT for SPD is behavioral activation, which involves gradually increasing activities and behaviors that the person has been avoiding or withdrawing from. This may include participating in social events, volunteering, or engaging in hobbies or interests. The therapist works with the individual to set achievable goals and encourages them to challenge their fears and negative thoughts as they work towards these goals.

CBT can be delivered in individual or group therapy sessions and may be combined with other treatment approaches, such as medication management or family therapy. The length and frequency of therapy sessions may vary depending on the individual's needs and goals.

Research has shown that CBT can be effective in reducing symptoms of SPD, including social isolation, depression, and anxiety. It can also improve overall functioning and quality of life for individuals with the disorder.

In conclusion, Cognitive Behavioral Therapy is a valuable tool for individuals with Schizoid Personality Disorder to challenge negative thinking patterns and behaviors, learn new coping skills, and gradually increase their engagement in social activities. With the help of a trained therapist, individuals can learn to manage their symptoms and improve their overall well-being.

Dialectical Behavior Therapy for Schizoid Personality Disorder

Dialectical Behavior Therapy (DBT) is a type of psychotherapy that was originally developed to treat borderline personality disorder (BPD). However, it has also been used to treat a variety of other mental health conditions, including Schizoid Personality Disorder (SPD). In this chapter, we will explore the basics of DBT and how it can help people with SPD.

DBT was developed by Marsha Linehan in the 1980s. It is a form of cognitive-behavioral therapy that emphasizes the importance of acceptance and mindfulness. DBT is based on the idea that some people are more emotionally sensitive than others, which can make it difficult for them to regulate their emotions. DBT teaches people skills to help them regulate their emotions and cope with difficult situations.

The four main components of DBT are:

Mindfulness: Mindfulness is the practice of being present at the moment and accepting one's thoughts, feelings, and bodily sensations without judgment.

Distress Tolerance: Distress tolerance skills help people cope with intense emotions and difficult situations. These skills include distraction, self-soothing, and improving the moment.

Emotional Regulation: Emotional regulation skills help people manage their emotions effectively. These skills include identifying and labeling emotions, understanding the functions of emotions, and changing unwanted emotions.

Interpersonal Effectiveness: Interpersonal effectiveness skills help people communicate effectively and maintain healthy relationships. These skills include assertiveness, active listening, and setting boundaries.

DBT is typically conducted in both individual and group therapy sessions. During individual therapy sessions, the therapist helps the person with SPD develop skills to cope with difficult emotions and improve relationships. Group therapy sessions provide a supportive environment where people can practice their skills and learn from others.

DBT for SPD focuses on developing social skills and improving social functioning. People with SPD often struggle with interpersonal relationships and may have difficulty expressing emotions or engaging in social interactions. DBT can help people with SPD learn to communicate more effectively, set boundaries, and develop closer relationships with others.

DBT can also help people with SPD develop emotion regulation skills. People with SPD often experience intense emotions, but they may not know how to identify or express them. DBT teaches people how to identify and label their emotions, as well as how to manage them effectively.

Finally, DBT can help people with SPD develop mindfulness skills. Mindfulness can be particularly helpful for people with SPD because it can help them stay present in social situations and regulate their emotions effectively. Mindfulness exercises such as deep breathing, body scanning, and meditation can help people with SPD develop a greater sense of self-awareness and improve their ability to regulate their emotions.

In conclusion, DBT is an effective form of therapy for people with Schizoid Personality Disorder. It can help people with SPD develop social skills, regulate their emotions, and improve their overall quality of life. If you have SPD, consider speaking with a mental health professional about whether DBT may be right for you.

Group Therapy for Schizoid Personality Disorder

Group therapy is a form of psychotherapy that involves a group of individuals who come together to discuss their emotional difficulties, and it is often used as a treatment option for individuals with various mental health issues, including schizoid personality disorder (SPD). In group therapy, participants are encouraged to share their thoughts and feelings with others, and they can receive feedback and support from the other members of the group.

Group therapy can be beneficial for individuals with SPD because it can help them to develop social skills and improve their ability to connect with others. It can also help individuals with SPD to feel less isolated and more understood, as they can interact with others who may share similar struggles.

One of the key benefits of group therapy is that it provides a safe and supportive environment for individuals with SPD to practice and improve their social skills. This can include practicing initiating and maintaining conversations, sharing personal experiences, and expressing emotions. By practicing these skills in a supportive and non-judgmental setting, individuals with SPD can gain more confidence in their ability to interact with others.

In addition, group therapy can also help individuals with SPD to feel less alone and more connected to others. It can be comforting for individuals with SPD to realize that they are not the only ones who struggle with social interaction and that others understand their experiences. This can help to reduce feelings of isolation and improve overall emotional well-being.

Group therapy can also be effective in helping individuals with SPD to identify and challenge negative thought patterns and beliefs about themselves and others. Through group discussions and interactions, individuals with SPD can gain insight into their thought patterns and learn new ways of thinking about themselves and others.

It is important to note that group therapy is not a one-size-fits-all treatment option for individuals with SPD, and it may not be effective for everyone. Some individuals with SPD may struggle with the idea of sharing their thoughts and feelings with others or may feel uncomfortable in a group setting. However, for those who are open to the idea of group therapy, it can be a valuable tool in improving social skills and reducing feelings of isolation.

When considering group therapy as a treatment option for SPD, it is important to find a therapist who has experience working with individuals with SPD and who can create a safe and supportive environment for group members. It may also be helpful to find a group that is specifically geared towards individuals with SPD, as this can provide a more tailored experience and allow for more targeted discussions and interventions.

Overall, group therapy can be a valuable treatment option for individuals with schizoid personality disorder, as it can help them to improve their social skills, reduce feelings of isolation, and gain insight into their thought patterns and beliefs. By finding a supportive and experienced therapist, individuals with SPD can work towards improving their emotional well-being and developing more fulfilling relationships with others.

Medication Options for Schizoid Personality Disorder

Medication is not typically considered the primary treatment option for schizoid personality disorder. However, certain medications may be prescribed to help alleviate specific symptoms associated with the disorder. It is important to note that medication should always be taken under the guidance and supervision of a qualified healthcare provider.

Some of the medications that may be used in the treatment of schizoid personality disorder include:

Antidepressants: These medications are often used to treat symptoms of depression that may be associated with schizoid personality disorder. Antidepressants work by increasing the levels of certain chemicals in the brain that help regulate mood, such as serotonin and norepinephrine.

Anxiolytics: Also known as anti-anxiety medications, anxiolytics may be prescribed to help manage feelings of anxiety that may accompany schizoid personality disorder. These medications work by reducing activity in the brain that is responsible for producing feelings of anxiety.

Antipsychotics: While not commonly used to treat schizoid personality disorder, antipsychotic medications may be prescribed to alleviate symptoms such as delusions or hallucinations. These medications work by blocking certain receptors in the brain that are associated with psychotic symptoms.

It is important to note that medication is not a cure for schizoid personality disorder, and should always be used in conjunction with other forms of treatment such as therapy and lifestyle changes. It is also important to discuss any potential risks and side effects associated with medication use with a healthcare provider.

Additionally, it is important to note that self-medication with alcohol or other substances should be avoided, as it can exacerbate symptoms of schizoid personality disorder and increase the risk of negative health outcomes. If you are struggling with substance use, it is important to seek help from a qualified healthcare provider or addiction specialist.

Schizoid Personality Disorder is a condition that is often misunderstood and stigmatized in society. However, it is important to recognize that people with this disorder can lead fulfilling lives, just like anyone else. Embracing one's individuality can be a key component to managing Schizoid Personality Disorder and achieving a sense of well-being.

Individuality is the quality or character of a person that distinguishes them from others. For someone with Schizoid Personality Disorder, this often manifests as a preference for solitary activities and a lack of interest in social relationships. While this may be seen as "abnormal" by society, individuals with Schizoid Personality Disorder need to recognize that their preferences are valid and can be a source of strength.

One way to embrace individuality with Schizoid Personality Disorder is to focus on personal interests and hobbies. Many individuals with this disorder have a deep interest in specific topics or activities and may find great fulfillment in pursuing these passions. This can provide a sense of purpose and direction, as well as a feeling of accomplishment.

Another way to embrace individuality is to recognize and appreciate one's unique perspectives and ways of thinking. People with Schizoid Personality Disorder may have a more detached and objective perspective on the world around them, which can be valuable in certain situations. This can also help to reduce feelings of inadequacy or inferiority that may arise from comparing oneself to more socially-oriented individuals.

It is also important for individuals with Schizoid Personality Disorder to practice self-compassion and acceptance. It can be easy to feel isolated or like an outsider, especially in a world that values social connections so highly. However, it is important to recognize that one's preferences and needs are valid and deserving of respect. This can involve setting boundaries with others and learning to say "no" to social situations that do not align with one's needs or desires.

Therapy can also be a valuable tool for embracing individuality with Schizoid Personality Disorder. Working with a therapist can help individuals explore and better understand their preferences, strengths, and limitations. It can also provide a safe and supportive space to practice asserting one's needs and boundaries.

Ultimately, embracing individuality with Schizoid Personality Disorder involves recognizing that there is no "right" or "wrong" way to be in the world. Each person has their own unique set of strengths and challenges, and it is up to them to define what a fulfilling and meaningful life looks like. By accepting and valuing themselves for who they are, individuals with Schizoid Personality Disorder can find greater self-confidence, purpose, and well-being.

Maintaining Progress and Growth with Schizoid Personality Disorder

Maintaining progress and growth with Schizoid Personality Disorder can be a challenging process, but it is possible with continued dedication and support. Here are some tips to help you continue moving forward:

Stay committed to therapy: Whether you are engaging in individual or group therapy, it is important to stay committed to the process. Therapy can help you continue to develop coping strategies and work on communication skills that will help you in your relationships and life in general.

Stay connected with others: While it may not be easy for someone with Schizoid Personality Disorder to form deep emotional connections, it is important to stay connected with others in some way. This can include joining clubs or groups that cater to your interests, volunteering, or simply spending time with family or friends. By staying connected with others, you can help reduce feelings of isolation and loneliness.

Continue to practice mindfulness: Mindfulness practices, such as meditation, can help you remain present at the moment and help reduce symptoms of anxiety or depression. Incorporating mindfulness into your daily routine can help you stay grounded and centered.

Be patient with yourself: Changing ingrained thought patterns and behaviors take time and effort. It is important to be patient with yourself and not get discouraged if progress feels slow. Celebrate small successes along the way and keep working towards your goals.

Engage in self-care: Taking care of yourself both physically and emotionally is crucial for maintaining progress and growth. This can include exercise, a healthy diet, getting enough sleep, and engaging in activities that bring you joy.

Continue to learn about Schizoid Personality Disorder: Understanding your condition and how it impacts you can help you continue to develop effective coping strategies. You can read books, attend workshops or conferences, or connect with online support groups.

Celebrate your individuality: Embrace the unique qualities that make you who you are. Recognize that having Schizoid Personality Disorder does not define you as a person. Celebrate your individuality and work towards living a life that is fulfilling and meaningful to you.

In conclusion, maintaining progress and growth with Schizoid Personality Disorder requires continued effort, patience, and support. By staying committed to therapy, staying connected with others, practicing mindfulness, being patient with yourself, engaging in self-care, continuing to learn, and celebrating your individuality, you can continue to move forward and live a fulfilling life. Remember that progress is not always linear and setbacks may occur, but with persistence and support, you can continue to make progress towards your goals.